With Friendly Wishes

FAVORITE SAYINGS
TO WARM THE HEART

Selected by

Daniel Drake

Illustrated by

Pat Paris

If a task is once begun,
Never leave it till it's done.
Be the labor great or small,
Do it well or not at all.

Oh, better than the minting

Of a gold-crowned king

Is the safe-kept memory

Of a lovely thing.

The world's a very happy place
Where everyone should
dance and sing,
And always have a smiling face
And never sulk for anything.

Wealth is not his who has it,
But his who enjoys it.

Think of three things:
Whence you came,
Where you are going
And to whom you must account.

There is a time for some things,
And a time for all things;
A time for great things
And a time for small things.

If you would reap praise
You must sow the seeds:
Gentle words
And useful deeds.

A true friend is
the best possession.